I'm making silly alphabet soup. First I need to put **a**pples, **b**ananas and **c**arrots into the soup pot.

Dd

Ee

Ff

Gg

Hh

Hmmm, this soup needs some ice cream, jam and ketchup.

Ii

Jj

Jam

Kk

Ketchup

This soup smells good... I'll add lemons, milk and noodles.

Ll

Mm

MILK

Nn

Here are some tasty onions, a pineapple and some quiche.

Oo

Pp

Qq

I can't forget to add radishes, a sandwich and tomatoes.

Rr

Ss

Tt

It's time to stir in unsweetened chocolate, vegetable oil and some watermelon.

U u

V v

Vegetable Oil

W w

Xx

Yy

Zz